BAKER BECAME A REGULAR CATECHIST AT LIMESTONE HILL, TEACHING SUNDAY CATECHISM CLASSES FOR SEVERAL MONTHS.

THREE YEARS LATER IN 1868...

WHERE ARE YOU GOING?

ON A RELIGIOUS *RETREAT?*

YES, A RETREAT AT ST. JOHN'S COLLEGE IN FORDHAM...

...I'LL BE GONE FOR *FIVE* DAYS, SO YOU'LL BE IN CHARGE!

WHEN I'M GONE...

...TRY NOT TO LOSE ALL OF OUR *MONEY!*

YOU BETTER NOT GET ANY STRANGE *IDEAS* ON THAT RETREAT...

...LIKE LEAVING ME TO BECOME A *PRIEST!*

AFTER ORDINATION, FATHER BAKER BECAME THE ASSISTANT TO FATHER HINES AT ST. JOHN'S PROTECTORY AND ORPHAN ASYLUM AT LIMESTONE HILL.

GREAT TO SEE YOU!

NOW AS *FATHER* BAKER!

I AM GLAD TO HAVE YOUR *HELP* AGAIN AT LIMESTONE HILL.

FATHER HINES, WHY DID YOU PUT *BARS* ON THE WINDOWS?

IS THIS A *REFUGE* FOR TROUBLED BOYS OR A *PRISON?*

NO, NOT A PRISON...

THE PEOPLE ARE *AFRAID* THAT THESE *BAD* BOYS WILL TERRORIZE THE CITY IF THEY ARE LET LOOSE.

THERE ARE NO *BAD* BOYS!

WE NEED TO TREAT THEM LIKE *SONS,* AND NOT PRISONERS!

THESE BARS NEED TO BE *REMOVED!*

LET ME *SHOW* YOU THE BOYS FIRST, AND MAYBE THAT WILL *CHANGE* YOUR MIND.

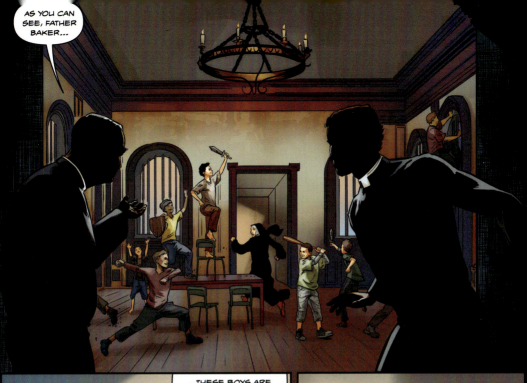

AS YOU CAN SEE, FATHER BAKER...

...THESE BOYS ARE *IMPOSSIBLE* TO CONTAIN WITH OUR LIMITED STAFF!

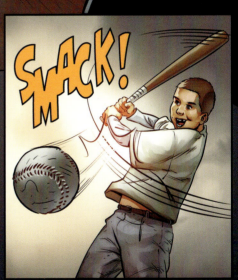

SMACK!

NOTHING IS *IMPOSSIBLE*...

...THEY ONLY NEED A *FATHER!*

IF I'M EVER IN *CHARGE* HERE...

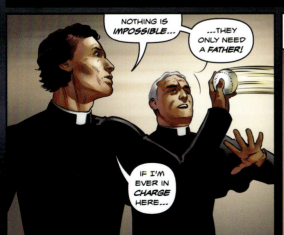

...I'LL TAKE THOSE BARS DOWN AND LET THE BOYS *LOOSE* OUTSIDE...

...AND TEACH THEM HOW TO BE *SONS* OF A LOVING AND MERCIFUL *FATHER.*

TO RAISE ENOUGH MONEY FOR NEEDED REPAIRS, FATHER BAKER ESTABLISHED THE ASSOCIATION OF OUR BLESSED LADY OF VICTORY AND WROTE TO POTENTIAL *DONORS*.

All I ask is that you pray th for the boys in my car donation if you c

THOUSANDS OF LETTERS WERE SENT OUT ALL OVER THE COUNTRY.

IS THIS ALL *YOUR* MAIL?

YES, FOR *TODAY*!

I'LL HAVE *MORE* FOR YOU TO SEND TOMORROW!

MANY RESPONDED TO FATHER BAKER'S APPEAL, AND ALL DEBTS WERE PAID.

THANK YOU!

YOU DID IT, FATHER BAKER!

NO, I HARDLY DID *ANYTHING*!

IT WAS OUR LADY WHO GRANTED *US* VICTORY!

KNOCK!
KNOCK!

COME IN!

FATHER...

...I CAN'T DO IT ANYMORE!

WAAAAAHHH!!

YOU CAN'T DO WHAT?

WHAT IS IT, DEAR CHILD?

I CAN'T CARE FOR MY OWN BABY!

MY PARENTS KICKED ME OUT OF THE HOUSE WHEN THEY FOUND OUT I WAS PREGNANT!

THEY EVEN PRESSURED ME TO GET RID OF HIM!

I—I COULDN'T DO IT...BUT I ALSO DON'T HAVE ANYWHERE TO GO OR ANYONE TO TURN TO.

YOU HAVE COME TO THE *RIGHT* PLACE...

...I KNEW SOMETHING WAS *MISSING* IN OUR COMMUNITY.

RIGHT NOW, WE SERVE CHILDREN FROM FIVE YEARS OLD UNTIL PAST THEIR FIFTEENTH BIRTHDAY...

...WE HAVE *NOTHING* IN PLACE FOR MOTHERS OR INFANTS IN NEED.

THAT CHANGES *TODAY!*

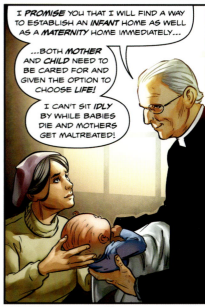

I *PROMISE* YOU THAT I WILL FIND A WAY TO ESTABLISH AN *INFANT* HOME AS WELL AS A *MATERNITY* HOME IMMEDIATELY...

...BOTH *MOTHER* AND *CHILD* NEED TO BE CARED FOR AND GIVEN THE OPTION TO CHOOSE *LIFE!*

I CAN'T SIT *IDLY* BY WHILE BABIES DIE AND MOTHERS GET MALTREATED!

THANK YOU, FATHER!

THIS IS *EXACTLY* WHAT I WAS HOPING AND PRAYING FOR!

SHORTLY AFTER, FATHER BAKER WAS ABLE TO SECURE THE FUNDS NECESSARY TO BUILD THE OUR LADY OF VICTORY INFANT HOME.

FATHER BAKER'S MASSIVE PROJECT STARTED IN 1921 WHEN PLANS FOR A NEW CHURCH WERE INITIATED.

I HAVE TRAVELED ALL OVER *EUROPE* AND THE CHURCH I HAVE DESIGNED WILL BE...

...THE MOST BEAUTIFUL SHRINE IN THE WORLD FOR NOTRE DAME DES VICTORIES!

PERFECT!

FOR THE MONEY HE NEEDED TO BUILD THE CHURCH, FATHER BAKER ONCE AGAIN TURNED TO HIS LOYAL PATRONS...

AFTER FIVE YEARS OF CONSTRUCTION, THE SHRINE TO OUR LADY OF VICTORY WAS COMPLETED.

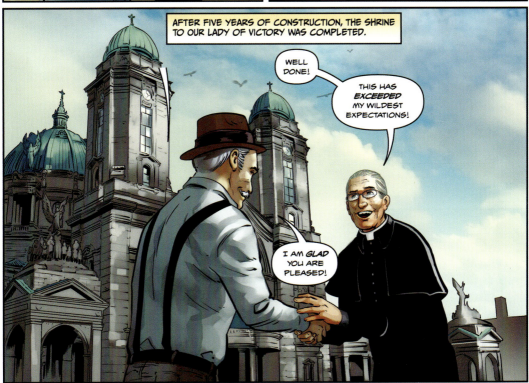

WELL DONE!

THIS HAS *EXCEEDED* MY WILDEST EXPECTATIONS!

I AM *GLAD* YOU ARE PLEASED!

THANK YOU, BLESSED MOTHER!!

YOU *ALWAYS* KEEP WATCH OVER US AND MAKE SURE ALL OF OUR NEEDS ARE MET!

I OWE EVERYTHING TO *YOU* AND YOUR INTERCESSION BEFORE GOD!

THE GREAT DEPRESSION, 1930.

FATHER BAKER COULDN'T SIT IDLY BY, IN THE MIDST OF SO MUCH SUFFERING, EVEN THOUGH HE WAS 88 YEARS OLD.

WELL BOYS...

...I HAD TO *SEE* IT FOR MYSELF.

MEN ARE OUT OF WORK AND MANY FAMILIES ARE *HOMELESS*, WITHOUT ANY FOOD OR SHELTER.

LOOK FATHER BAKER!

HE DOESN'T HAVE ANY *SHOES!*

AND IT'S ALMOST *CHRISTMAS!*

WILL THOSE CHILDREN GET ANY *PRESENTS?*

LET'S GO BACK TO THE PROTECTORY...

...WE HAVE *WORK* TO DO!

FATHER BAKER'S BOYS WENT TO WORK AND STARTED MAKING *SHOES* AND *CLOTHING* FOR THOSE IN NEED.

GEE FATHER, THIS FEELS EVEN BETTER THAN *GETTING* PRESENTS!

HE NAMED HIS NEW MINISTRY THE *CITY OF CHARITY*.

THANK YOU, FATHER!!

DON'T FORGET TO COME BACK ON *CHRISTMAS EVE* FOR A NICE, WARM DINNER!

MERRY CHRISTMAS!

BETWEEN 1930 AND 1933, FATHER BAKER'S "CITY OF CHARITY" WOULD GO ON TO SERVE 454,000 MEALS AND PROVIDE 20,000 NIGHTS OF LODGING, 4,625 PAIRS OF SHOES, 2,215 COATS, AND 1,500 FREE MEDICAL PROCEDURES TO THOSE IN NEED.

AFTER YOU FINISH YOUR MEAL, MAKE SURE YOUR LITTLE ONES EACH GET A *PRESENT* BEFORE THEY GO!

MERRY CHRISTMAS!

WOO HOO

YIPPEEE

FATHER BAKER DIED ON JULY 29, 1936, AT THE AGE OF 94...

HOW DID YOU KNOW HIM?

HE FED MY FAMILY WHEN I COULDN'T AFFORD TO.

...OVER A FOUR-DAY PERIOD, 400,000 MOURNERS LINED THE STREETS TO SEE FATHER BAKER FOR ONE LAST TIME.

HE REACHED OUT TO ME WHEN I HAD NOTHING.

HIS CHARITABLE WORK LEFT A DEEP IMPACT UPON ALL THE PEOPLE HE SERVED, AND THEY DEEPLY MISSED HIM.

HE GAVE ME A HOME WHEN I HAD NOWHERE TO GO.

THE BOYS OF HIS INSTITUTIONS ESPECIALLY MISSED HIS JOVIAL AND LOVING PRESENCE.

HE WAS OUR CHAMPION.

HE WAS OUR INSPIRATION.

HE WAS OUR HERO.

† FATHER BAKER

FATHER BAKER'S LEGACY OF CARING CONTINUES TODAY...

... THE OLV ORGANIZATIONS CARRY ON HIS WORK TO THIS DAY, PROMOTING DEVOTION TO OUR LADY OF VICTORY AND PROVIDING SERVICES TO 10,000-12,000 CHILDREN, ADULTS, AND FAMILIES IN NEED EACH YEAR.

HIS CAUSE FOR CANONIZATION WAS OPENED IN 1987, AND HE WAS DECLARED "VENERABLE" IN 2011 BY POPE BENEDICT XVI.

MANY HOPE THAT SOMEDAY FATHER BAKER WILL BE RAISED TO THE ALTARS BY THE CHURCH AS ONE OF THE *SAINTS* IN HEAVEN.

HE WAS A SERVANT OF GOD, A FRIEND TO THE LOWLY, AND A FATHER TO THE FATHERLESS.

THE LIFE OF
FR. NELSON BAKER

1842 –
Nelson Henry Baker is born on February 16.

1851 –
Originally baptized into the Lutheran faith, Nelson is baptized as a Catholic at the age of nine.

1863 –
Baker enlists in the Union Army during the Civil War.

1863 -
Upon his return, he enters a business partnership with a friend and starts Meyer & Baker, a grain and feed enterprise.

1869 –
Wrestling with a call to a vocation, Nelson goes on a steamer excursion through the Great Lakes in the summer to "clear his mind." He returns with the decision to become a priest. In September, he enters the seminary at the "advanced" age of 27.

1874 –
He is part of an American Pilgrimage to Europe. While in France, he is inspired to devote his life to the Blessed Mother under the title of Our Lady of Victory.

1876 –
Father Nelson Baker is ordained on March 19.

1876 –
He arrives at his first assignment out of the seminary, the Limestone Hill institutions, consisting of a small orphanage and protectory for "willful" boys.

1881 –
Concerned by the growing debt of the institutions, Father Baker requests a transfer and is sent to St. Mary's Parish in Corning, N.Y.

1882 –
He is sent back to Limestone Hill, as Superintendent, by Bishop Stephen Ryan.

1883 –
Father Baker founds the Spiritual Association of Our Lady of Victory, a direct-mail club for donors who would support his mission. The idea quickly improves the financial state of the organization, and it expands.

1908 –
OLV Infant Home is dedicated and opened to care for unwed mothers and their babies.

1922 –
Through his national donor magazine, the *Annals*, Father Baker asks supporters to contribute $10 to "furnish a block of marble" for the building of the OLV shrine.

1925 –
Construction of the Basilica is completed just in time for Christmas Mass.

1936 –
Father Baker dies on July 29 at age 94.

THE STAGES OF
CANONIZATION

 Servant of God
Promoter group (diocese, parish, religious congregation, etc.) requests an investigation by the Holy See; if granted, the candidate receives the title: Servant of God.

 Venerable
The declaration of a person's heroic virtues and sanctity of life, after which his/her title is: Venerable.

 Blessed
Once a miracle is attributed to the intercession of the candidate, the candidate is declared: Blessed.

Saint
After a second miracle is attributed to the candidate's intercession, the Holy Father declares the candidate to be a Saint.

Venerable Nelson Baker's Cause for Canonization was started in 1987 when he was named "Servant of God" by Vatican officials. He earned the title "Venerable" in 2011, when Pope Benedict XVI conferred the title upon Father Baker after a thorough review of his life and writings.

This remarkable man, who is still known as the "Father of the Fatherless" and "Padre of the Poor" decades after his death, did so many things for so many people. And now, it is our time to help him. All are asked to incorporate Father Baker in their daily prayers, to say his prayer for canonization (below), or just share with God your hope that he be canonized. If you have a need, pray for Father Baker's intercession. And, of course, if you have a story, or first-hand knowledge of a potential cure or miracle that has occurred in his name, please let us know.

With joyful anticipation, we await that glorious day when Father Baker is officially declared Saint Nelson! For more information on his life, legacy and Cause for Canonization, be sure to check out www.fatherbaker.org.

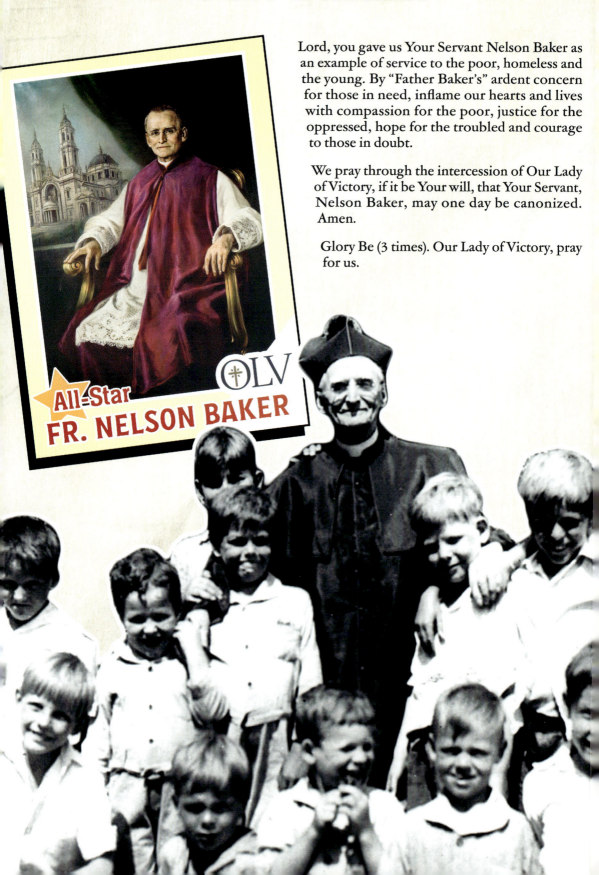

PRAY FOR THE CANONIZATION OF
FR. NELSON BAKER

Lord, you gave us Your Servant Nelson Baker as an example of service to the poor, homeless and the young. By "Father Baker's" ardent concern for those in need, inflame our hearts and lives with compassion for the poor, justice for the oppressed, hope for the troubled and courage to those in doubt.

We pray through the intercession of Our Lady of Victory, if it be Your will, that Your Servant, Nelson Baker, may one day be canonized. Amen.

Glory Be (3 times). Our Lady of Victory, pray for us.

All-Star **OLV**
FR. NELSON BAKER